Ten Cats
Have Hats

Ten Cats Have Hats

A Counting Book

by Jean Marzollo
Illustrated by David McPhail

SCHOLASTIC INC.
New York   Toronto   London   Auckland   Sydney

For Frank Hodge
—J.M.

For Ben—
"You can't throw the ball by me."
—D.M.

Text copyright © 1994 by Jean Marzollo.
Illustrations copyright © 1994 by David McPhail.
All rights reserved. Published by Scholastic Inc.
Printed in the U.S.A.
ISBN 0-590-47056-6

5 6 7 8 9 10   08   02

1 One bear has a chair,
but I have a hat.

2

Two ducks have trucks,
but I have a hat.

Three trees have bees,
but I have a hat.

4

Four stores have doors,
but I have a hat.

5

Five pigs have wigs,
but I have a hat.

6 Six bugs have rugs,
but I have a hat.

7

Seven goats have coats,
but I have a hat.

Eight crabs have cabs,
but I have a hat.

9

Nine snails have trails,
but I have a hat.

Ten cats have hats...

just like me.